THE GREAT BIBLE

DISCOVERY

THE SUFFERING AND THE GLORY

THE BIBLE IS A BEST-SELLER. IT IS ALSO ONE OF THE MASTER-WORKS OF WORLD LITERATURE - SO IMPORTANT THAT UNIVERSITIES TODAY TEACH 'NON-RELIGIOUS' BIBLE COURSES TO HELP STUDENTS WHO CHOOSE TO STUDY WESTERN LITERATURE.

THE BIBLE POSSESSES AN AMAZING POWER TO FASCINATE YOUNG AND OLD ALIKE.

ONE REASON FOR THIS UNIVERSAL APPEAL IS THAT IT DEALS WITH BASIC HUMAN LONGINGS, EMOTIONS, RELATIONSHIPS. 'ALL THE WORLD IS HERE.' ANOTHER REASON IS THAT SO MUCH OF THE BIBLE CONSISTS OF STORIES. THEY ARE FULL OF MEANING BUT EASY TO REMEMBER.

HERE ARE THOSE STORIES, PRESENTED SIMPLY AND WITH A MINIMUM OF EXPLANATION. WE HAVE LEFT THE TEXT TO SPEAK FOR ITSELF. GIFTED ARTISTS USE THE ACTION-STRIP TECHNIQUE TO BRING THE BIBLE'S DEEP MESSAGE TO READERS OF ALL AGES. THEIR DRAWINGS ARE BASED ON INFORMATION FROM ARCHAEOLOGICAL DISCOVERIES COVERING FIFTEEN CENTURIES.

AN ANCIENT BOOK - PRESENTED FOR THE PEOPLE OF THE SECOND MILLENNIUM. A RELIGIOUS BOOK - PRESENTED FREE FROM THE INTERPRETATION OF ANY PARTICULAR CHURCH. A UNIVERSAL BOOK - PRESENTED IN A FORM THAT ALL MAY ENJOY.

OM publishing
CARLISLE, UK

21

The Pharisees felt threatened by Jesus - his teaching differed from theirs in several ways, and he was very popular. They could not deny his power. But they concluded that when he cast out demons it was through Satan's power, not God's. The Temple authorities had their reasons for fearing his influence.

The Old Testament has a lot to say about the sufferings of the innocent. Isaac was an only son who was willing to be sacrificed. The Son of Man in Daniel 7 is the head of a line of faithful believers ill-treated by heathen kings. The prophecy of Isaiah speaks of a Servant of the Lord who would suffer and die because of the sins of others. Jesus went to his death willingly, although his disciples discouraged him. By giving his life he would set people free from the power of evil. Yet his prayer in Gethsemane shows how he feared what lay ahead of him.

He visited Jerusalem several times. He drove the traders out of the Temple. He warned that the Temple itself would be destroyed. On his last visit, crowds of Passover pilgrims waved palm branches to welcome him as messiah. These things made the Jewish leaders even more anxious and angry. When Jesus ate the sacred meal with his disciples he gave a new interpretation to the Passover. His death, he said would seal a covenant even greater than that Moses received at Sinai. But when he was arrested all but two of the disciples ran off.

The Jewish council or Sanhedrin condemned Jesus for blasphemy. Because they could not carry out the death penalty they handed him to the Roman governor as a political prisoner. Crucifixion was a routine - and agonizing - method of executing criminals who were not Roman citizens. Jesus suffered it alone, deserted by almost all his disciples.

The courageous women who had been the last to leave the cross were the first to visit his tomb. They were amazed and frightened to find it empty. The last thing anybody had expected was that Jesus might rise from the dead.

MATTHEW 13; 19; 21; 24; 26-27
MARK 10; 13-16
LUKE 10-13; 15; 18-19; 22-23
JOHN 3; 5-6; 8; 10-11; 18-19

THE SUFFERING AND THE GLORY

First published as *Découvrir la Bible* 1983

First edition © Librairie Larousse 1983

24-volume series adaptation by Mike Jacklin © Knowledge Unlimited 1994
This edition © OM Publishing 1995

01 00 99 98 97 96 95   7 6 5 4 3 2 1

OM Publishing is an imprint of Send the Light Ltd.,
P.O. Box 300, Carlisle, Cumbria CA3 0QS, U.K.

Introductions: Peter Cousins

British Library Cataloguing in Publication Data
A catalogue record for this book is available from the British Library
ISBN 1-85078-225-3

Printed in Singapore by Tien Wah Press (Pte) Ltd.

THE ROAD TO JERUSALEM

SCENARIO: Etienne DAHLER
DRAWING: Pierre FRISANO

ON HIS WAY TO JERUSALEM, JESUS WENT ON THROUGH SAMARIA.

A FEW DAYS LATER JESUS WENT TO PRAY BY HIMSELF. WHEN HIS DISCIPLES JOINED HIM...

THERE HE IS!

LORD, TEACH US HOW TO PRAY...

IT'S SIMPLE. SAY THIS:

FATHER! LET YOUR HOLY NAME BE HONOURED! LET YOUR KINGDOM COME!

GIVE US EACH DAY THE BREAD WE NEED. FORGIVE US OUR SINS, AS WE ALSO FORGIVE THOSE WHO SIN AGAINST US...

AND DO NOT BRING US TO HARD TESTING.

...THEN JESUS CONTINUED...

ASK, AND IT WILL BE GIVEN TO YOU! SEEK, AND YOU WILL FIND! KNOCK, AND IT WILL BE OPENED TO YOU!

THE DISCIPLES WERE QUIET FOR A LONG TIME...

5

ON THE WAY, AS THEY PASSED THROUGH A VILLAGE...

STOP, THIEF!

HE WENT THAT WAY!

IF THE MASTER OF THE HOUSE HAD KNOWN WHEN THE THIEF WAS COMING, HE WOULDN'T HAVE LET HIM BREAK THROUGH HIS WALL!

YOU MUST ALL BE READY! BECAUSE YOU DON'T KNOW WHEN THE SON OF MAN WILL COME.

AND THE KINGDOM OF GOD, WHEN WILL IT COME?

THE KINGDOM OF GOD? IT'S ALREADY AMONG YOU!

THAT DOESN'T MAKE SENSE!

ON THE OTHER HAND...

...IT SAYS A LOT ABOUT WHO HE CLAIMS TO BE...

THE JEWISH FESTIVAL HAD BEGUN. GOING UP TO THE TEMPLE, JESUS STOPPED AT THE POOL OF BETHESDA.

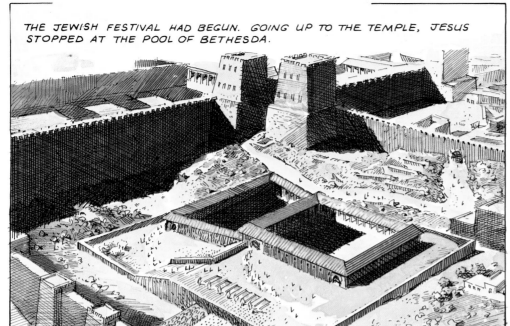

WHY ARE ALL THESE SICK PEOPLE HERE?

BECAUSE OF THE SIGNS... NOW AND AGAIN THE WATER BUBBLES. THE FIRST TO JUMP INTO THE POOL IS CURED!

DO YOU WANT TO BE HEALED?

YES! BUT I'VE NOBODY TO THROW ME INTO THE POOL WHEN THE WATER'S STIRRED UP!

GET UP, PICK UP YOUR MAT, AND WALK!

JESUS DISAPPEARED INTO THE CROWD.

I'M WALKING! I'VE BEEN LYING DOWN FOR SUCH A LONG TIME, AND LOOK: NOW I'M WALKING!

IT'S THE SABBATH!

YOU'RE NOT ALLOWED TO CARRY YOUR MAT!*

WHO HEALED YOU? WHAT'S HIS NAME?

I DON'T KNOW. ALL I KNOW IS THAT HE CURED ME!

* The law did not allow anything to be carried on the Sabbath.

8

WHILE JESUS WAS PASSING THROUGH THE VILLAGE OF BETHANY, A WOMAN CALLED MARTHA WENT UP TO HIM. SHE HAD A SISTER CALLED MARY.

IN THE EARLY MORNING JESUS WENT BACK TO THE TEMPLE. A CROWD GATHERED TO HEAR HIS TEACHING.

SUDDENLY...

THIS WOMAN WAS CAUGHT IN THE ACT OF ADULTERY.

THE LAW OF MOSES SAYS WE MUST STONE HER TO DEATH...

AND YOU, WHAT DO YOU SAY?

LET HIM WHO'S NEVER SINNED THROW THE FIRST STONE!

E BY ONE THE PHARISEES ALKED AWAY, STARTING TH THE OLDEST.

WOMAN, WHERE ARE YOUR ACCUSERS? DID NO ONE CONDEMN YOU?

NO, LORD.

I DON'T CONDEMN YOU EITHER. GO, AND DON'T SIN AGAIN.

WHILE JESUS WAS WALKING THROUGH A VILLAGE, A GROUP OF CHILDREN RAN TO HIM. THE DISCIPLES CHASED THEM AWAY.

NOW, YOU CHILDREN, STAND BACK!

WHY CHASE THEM AWAY? LET THE LITTLE ONES COME TO ME...

THE KINGDOM OF GOD'S FOR THEM AND THOSE LIKE THEM!

FURTHER ON...

MASTER! WHAT MUST I DO TO HAVE ETERNAL LIFE?

IF YOU WANT TO HAVE LIFE, KEEP THE COMMANDMENTS!

I'VE DONE THAT... WHAT MORE MUST I DO?

IF YOU WANT TO BE PERFECT, GO AND SELL EVERYTHING YOU HAVE AND GIVE THE MONEY TO THE POOR; THEN FOLLOW ME...

I TELL YOU AGAIN: IT'S EASIER FOR A CAMEL TO GO THROUGH THE EYE OF A NEEDLE THAN FOR A RICH PERSON TO ENTER THE KINGDOM OF GOD.

THEN WHO CAN BE SAVED?

THINGS THAT ARE IMPOSSIBLE FOR PEOPLE ARE POSSIBLE FOR GOD!

THERE, SEE!

A LITTLE LATER...

MARTHA AND MARY SENT US... LAZARUS, THEIR BROTHER...

LORD, THE ONE YOU LOVE IS ILL!

COME AT ONCE...

THIS ILLNESS ISN'T FATAL. IT'LL SHOW THE GLORY OF GOD!

JESUS LET TWO DAYS PASS, THEN...

LET'S GO!

WE'RE GOING BACK TO JUDAEA.

BUT, RABBI, YOU WERE NEARLY STONED THERE, AND YOU WANT TO GO BACK?

UR FRIEND LAZARUS, IS DEAD.

AFTER WALKING FOR ONE DAY, THEY REACHED BETHANY.

LORD, IF YOU'D BEEN HERE, MY BROTHER WOULDN'T HAVE DIED!

MARTHA...

YOUR BROTHER WILL RISE AGAIN!

YES, I KNOW... ON THE LAST DAY...

17

IN JERUSALEM THE PRIESTS AND THE PHARISEES MET WITH THE JEWISH COUNCIL.

IF WE LET HIM GO ON LIKE THIS, EVERYONE WILL END UP BELIEVING IN HIM!

IT WOULD BE BETTER FOR ONE MAN TO DIE, RATHER THAN A WHOLE NATION.

ROME WILL ACCUSE US...

...OF REBELLION, AND DESTROY OUR TEMPLE AND OUR NATION.

JESUS WENT AWAY TO THE NEAR-BY VILLAGE CALLED EPHRAIM, THEN TO JERICHO.

I HEAR A NOISE. WHAT'S HAPPENING?

JESUS OF NAZARETH'S COMING ...

JESUS, SON OF DAVID, HAVE PITY ON ME!

JESUS! BLESS MY SON!

OVER HERE, MASTER!

WHAT DO YOU WANT ME TO DO FOR YOU?

LORD, GIVE ME BACK MY SIGHT.

SEE! YOUR FAITH HAS SAVED YOU!

BARTIMAEUS WAS HEALED IMMEDIATELY, AND BEGAN TO FOLLOW JESUS.

SOON JESUS LEFT JERICHO FOR JERUSALEM.

IN A FEW DAYS THE SON OF MAN WILL BE HANDED OVER TO THE PRIESTS AND THE SCRIBES, WHO'LL PUT HIM TO DEATH.

IN SIGHT OF BETHANY...

GO INTO THE VILLAGE, WHERE YOU'LL FIND A DONKEY. UNTIE IT, AND BRING IT HERE.

HOW DID HE KNOW THE DONKEY WAS THERE, AND THAT ITS OWNER WOULD GIVE IT TO US?

I DON'T KNOW, BUT THE LORD NEEDS IT!

LET'S GO TO JERUSALEM...

IT'S JESUS! THE ONE WHO RAISED LAZARUS!

BLESSED BE THE SON OF DAVID!

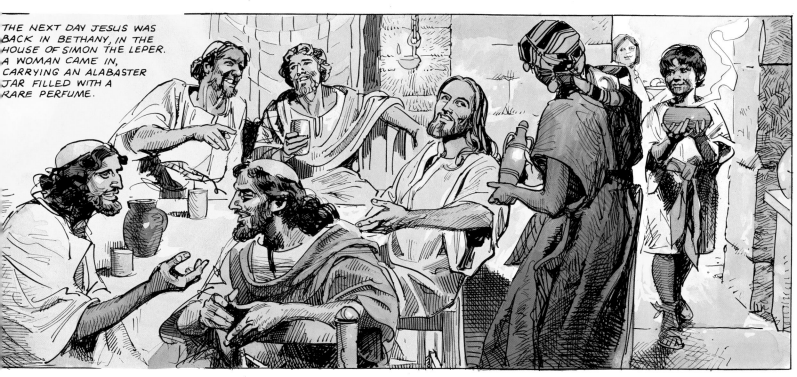

THE NEXT DAY JESUS WAS BACK IN BETHANY, IN THE HOUSE OF SIMON THE LEPER. A WOMAN CAME IN, CARRYING AN ALABASTER JAR FILLED WITH A RARE PERFUME.

SUDDENLY...

WHY WASTE HIS EXPENSIVE PERFUME? IT'S MADNESS!

SHE'S ANOINTED MY BODY, TO PREPARE IT AHEAD OF TIME FOR MY BURIAL.

THEN JUDAS WENT TO FIND THE HIGH PRIESTS, TO HAND JESUS OVER TO THEM.

THE PASSION

COME! EVERYTHING'S READY.

SOON IT WAS THE FEAST OF UNLEAVENED BREAD, WHEN THE JEWS CELEBRATED THE PASSOVER. JESUS SENT TWO DISCIPLES INTO JERUSALEM TO GET THE FESTIVAL MEAL READY. WHEN THEY RETURNED...

SCENARIO: Etienne DAHLER
DRAWING: Pierre FRISANO

IT'S HERE, IN THE UPPER ROOM.

I'VE SO LOOKED FORWARD TO CELEBRATING THIS PASSOVER WITH YOU.

AS YOU SEE, MASTER, NOTHING'S MISSING.

...NOTHING EXCEPT THE LAMB...

IT'S ROASTING DOWNSTAIRS.

ANNAS THEN SENT JESUS, HIS HANDS STILL BOUND, TO CAIAPHAS, THE HIGH PRIEST THAT YEAR.

IT MUST BE IMPORTANT, TO BE DISTURBING THE HIGH PRIEST AT THIS HOUR!

GO IN QUICKLY! THEY'RE WAITIN' FOR YOU!

HAVE YOU NOTHING TO SAY IN YOUR DEFENCE?

I HOPE YOU'LL EXPLAIN YOURSELF TO THE **SANHEDRIN*** IN THE MORNING.

* The Jewish council.

MEANWHILE KEEP HIM LOCKED UP!

SAVE ME, MY GOD! THE WATER IS UP TO MY NECK. IT IS FOR YOUR SAKE I HAVE BEEN INSULTED. I HAVE BECOME A STRANGER TO MY BROTHERS.

MY DEVOTION TO YOUR TEMPLE BURNS IN ME LIKE A FIRE; THE INSULTS WHICH ARE HURLED AT YOU FALL ON ME.

Psalm 69

HURRY UP! WE'VE GOT TO BE DONE BY SUNSET, AND THERE ARE TWO OTHERS TO BE EXECUTED AS WELL!

HE'S IN A BAD WAY! WILL HE LAST TO THE END?

THEN THE ROAD OF THE CROSS BEGAN, LEADING THE CONDEMNED MEN THROUGH THE STREETS TO THE PLACE OF EXECUTION.

STAND BACK! LET THEM PASS!

EXHAUSTED BY THE WHIPPING, JESUS FELL.

IF HE DOESN'T GET HELP, HE'LL DIE ON THE WAY!

YOU THERE,* CARRY THE CROSS FOR HIM.

*Simon of Cyrene.

WOMEN OF JERUSALEM, DON'T CRY FOR ME! CRY FOR YOURSELVES AND YOUR CHILDREN!

COME ON, MOVE!